Clever **K**ids

Study Skills
Ages 5-7

World Book, Inc.
Chicago London Sydney Toronto

For information on other World Book products,
call **1-800-255-1750, ext. 2238.**

World Book, Inc.
525 W. Monroe
Chicago, IL 60661

ISBN: 0-7166-9208-2
LC: 95-61966

Printed in the United States of America

2 3 4 5 6 7 8 9 10 99 98 97 96

Contents

All About You..4-5

Who Are You?..6-7

Show Off Your Name 8-9

Make a Soft Sculpture of You 10-11

Growing . . . Up 12-13

A Secret Hiding Box................................14-15

What Do You Think? 16

Neighborhood News 17

A Home in a Box 18-19

Map Your Neighborhood............................20-21

Playground Play...22-23

Neighborhood Post Office 24-25

Neighborhood Patchwork 26-27

How to Make a Book...............................28-30

What Do You Think? 31

All About You

Nobody else is just like you.

Nobody else has

⭐ **the same face,**

⭐ **the same hands,**

⭐ **the same feet,**

⭐ **the same voice,**

⭐ **or the same laugh as you do.**

And nobody knows more about you than you do!

How can you let other people get to know you? You can tell them about yourself. Or you can do some of the activities in this book. Then you'll find out more about yourself—and so will your family and friends!

Preview

Before you begin, look over pages 6 to 15. Read the titles and look closely at the pictures. Which activities would you like to do? Pick the ones you like best or do them all!

Who **A**re **Y**ou?

YOU NEED:

★ Pencil or pen
★ Paper or index cards
★ Pipe cleaners or string
★ Tape
★ Glue
★ Crayons or markers
★ Scissors (optional)
★ Stapler (optional)

What's your favorite color? What's your
favorite food? What's your favorite
book? Your favorite things are part
of what makes you, *you.* So are
your not-so-favorite things!

Review the "Nobody else" list on page 4. What other things about you are unlike anybody else? Copy or trace the web above onto a sheet of paper or put each heading on an index card. (You can attach the cards later with pipe cleaners or string.) Write down the things about you that fit into each category. You can even add categories or change them to suit yourself.

Another Idea

You may want to cut out each list and paste it onto a sheet of paper. Then draw pictures to illustrate the things you listed. You can staple the pages together to make a book about you.

Study Tip: Sort into Groups

When you have a lot of information to use, it helps to put it into groups. This is called *categorizing*.

Here's how to make a web about another topic:

★ Write your topic in the middle of a sheet of paper.
★ Draw lines, or spokes, coming out from your topic.
★ Write the name of a group at the end of each spoke.
★ Then list the things that go into each group. It's fine if some things fit into more than one group.

Show **O**ff **Y**our **N**ame

YOU NEED:
★ Pencil
★ Construction paper, poster board, or cardboard
★ Colorful markers
★ Glue or glue stick
★ A piece of yarn about 2 feet long
★ Scissors
★ A hole punch
★ A thumbtack or tape

What do you have now that you can keep for the rest of your life?

Your name! Show it off by making a name sign.

You can make all kinds of name signs. Here are two ideas.

Jazzy Sign

1. Write your name in large letters across the middle of a sheet of paper. You might want to use a pencil so that you can erase mistakes.

2. When your name looks just right, draw an outline around each letter, like this.

3. Go over your outlines in black or another dark color. Then color between the lines using bright colors.

You might want to use different colored yarn to outline and fill in your name. Go over your lines with glue or a glue stick. Then glue the yarn in place.

Poem Sign

1. Write your name down the left side of your piece of paper.

2. Think of ways to describe yourself. You might look back on the web you made in the last activity. For each letter in your name, write a word across the paper that describes you.

You might want to use one color for the letters in your name and other colors for the letters in the words.

3. Then decide what you want to do with the rest of the space on your sign. Here are some ideas:

★ Draw little pictures of yourself doing things.
★ Draw pictures of your favorite things.
★ Make designs.
★ Cut a fancy border around the edge of your sign.

4. Have someone help you punch holes in the top corners. Tie the ends of your yarn to each hole.

5. Hang your sign from a piece of tape or a doorknob. Or, have a grown-up help you hang it from a thumbtack.

Study Tip: Planning

Why is it important to plan ahead? How does it help to gather all the things you need before you begin a project? Well, for one thing, you don't have to get up and down all the time while you're working. Also, you wouldn't get too far along before finding out that you don't have everything you need to finish the project.

★ Read the materials list.
★ Gather the materials.
★ If you're missing something, get it or think of a replacement.
★ Then make your project.
★ When your project is finished, put everything back where you found it. Then your materials will be ready for next time.

Make a Soft Sculpture of You

YOU NEED:

★ One leg from a pair of pantyhose or one nylon stocking (get permission first)
★ Stuffing, such as batting, scraps of cloth, or shredded newspaper
★ Some of the following: felt, yarn, glue, markers, paint, old magazines (get permission to cut these up)
★ A square piece of heavy cardboard

Have you ever seen a statue of just a head? That kind of statue is called a *bust*. A bust shows what someone's face and head look like. Many busts are carved out of stone or wood, but you can make a bust of your head that's as soft as a pillow.

1. Stuff the pantyhose leg or stocking with batting, scraps of cloth, or shredded newspaper.

2. Tie a knot in the bottom to keep the stuffing in.

3. To make your bust stand up, you need to make a base. Ask an adult to make a hole in the center of your square of cardboard. Hold the sculpture at the neck and fold the bottom around itself. Tuck the end into the hole. Now you have a base.

4. Decorate your soft sculpture to make it look like you. You could use yarn for hair. You can paint or draw your ears, nose, mouth, and eyes; cut out felt pieces and glue them on; or cut out pictures of models in magazines.

Study Tip: Using Pictures

Do you ever look at pictures to figure out what's happening in a story or to help you follow directions? Pictures can make stories or information easier to understand.

★ Think about why the pictures are there. Are they included for your enjoyment? Do they show you how to do something? Do they show you how something works?

★ If you're having trouble understanding what you are reading, try drawing a picture of what you think is being described. If you have trouble coming up with a picture, reread the part that confuses you.

★ Ask for help if you need it. Explain exactly what the problem is.

★ Knowing what the pictures are supposed to do will help you when you read.

Growing...Up!

YOU NEED:
★ A piece of shelf paper 5 feet long
★ A pencil
★ Tape
★ A ruler
★ A tape measure (optional)

Did you ever put on a favorite
shirt—one you wore last year
or even last month—and it didn't fit?
What happened? You grew!

Every day you grow a little. Your hands grow a little bit bigger, your shoulders grow a little bit wider, and all of you grows a little bit taller.

Look through photo albums. How have you changed since you were a baby? Compare what you weighed when you were born to what you weigh today. How long were you when you were born? How tall are you today?

Here's a way to keep track of how you grow.

1. Write "How I Grow" at the top of your shelf paper, or make up your own title. You can decorate the top area, too, if you want.

2. Pick a place no one will run into, like a closet door, and tape your paper up. Have someone help you. Make sure the bottom of your paper is at floor level.

3. Stand up straight against the paper. Have someone put a ruler flat on your head, then draw a line where the ruler hits the paper.

4. Next to the line, write the date and your age.

5. Measure yourself every year on that exact same date. (You can measure yourself more often if you like.) Watch yourself grow!

Another Idea

Keep track of how your hands grow. Trace your hands on a large piece of paper. Whenever you measure how tall you've grown, trace your hands again. Put your hand right on top of the first tracing. What do you expect to see?

Study Tip: Predicting

When you're reading a book or watching a movie, do you ever try to figure out what's going to happen next? How about when something happens in real life? Do you ever guess how someone might act?

★ Trying to figure out what's going to happen is called *predicting*.
★ You make predictions based on what you know or what experiences you've had.

It's not important whether your prediction is what really happens in the story—or in life—although you might sometimes think that your prediction would have made a better ending. The important thing is that you use clues to draw conclusions or make predictions.

A Secret Hiding Box

YOU NEED:

★ A box large enough for you to fit inside
★ Scissors
★ Markers
★ Paints
★ Construction paper
★ Paste
★ Scraps of material (optional)
★ Table (optional)
★ Sheet (optional)

Do you have a place where you can go to be alone? A place to keep

all the special things you've made? A place where you can tell

secrets to a friend?

Everyone needs a special place.
Here's a way to make one.

1. Have a grown-up cut the flaps off
your box.

2. Draw a door. Have a grown-up cut
and fold it. Then draw some
windows. Have a grown-up cut those
out too.

3. Decorate your box any way you
want. Use markers, paints, and
construction paper to make bricks,
wood, or designs. If you have any
scraps of material, tape them up to
make curtains.

4. You might want to hang your name
sign on your door. Put anything else
inside that will make your box seem
special—your book about yourself,
your soft sculpture, or other things
that make you feel good.

14

Things you can do inside your box:

- ★ Tell stories to your teddy bear.
- ★ Read (make sure you have enough light from a window or a strong flashlight).
- ★ Write secret notes.
- ★ Tell secrets to a friend.
- ★ Pretend you're a troll and this is where you really live.
- ★ Take a nap.

Another Idea

If you don't have a box or if a grown-up is not around to help, you can make a secret place out of a table and sheet.

Study Tip: Brainstorming

Do you ever have trouble coming up with ideas? One way to get them is to brainstorm. For example, suppose you are going on a trip and you need some ideas for things to pack.

- ★ Get a piece of paper and a pencil. Jot down everything you might take along. Don't worry about whether it's a good idea or a bad idea. Just write down everything that pops into your head.
- ★ When you can't think of one more thing, look over your list. Pick out the ideas you especially like, cross out the others and start packing.

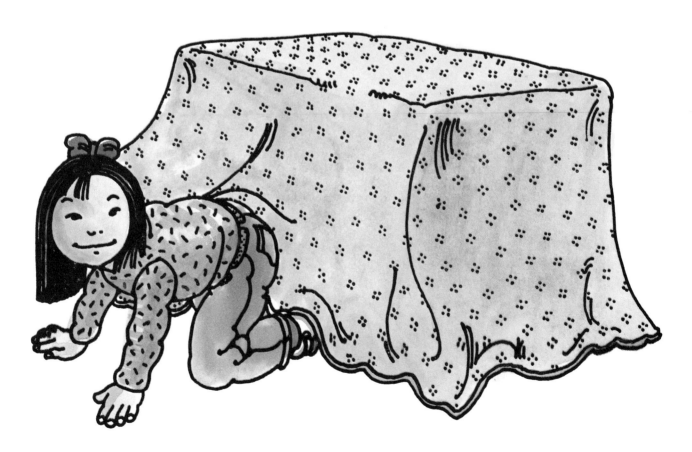

What **D**o **Y**ou **T**hink?

Now that you've thought about yourself, tell what you think about

this section. Write or draw your answers.

These are the activities I did:

This one was the most fun:

I am most proud of:

Here's something I learned about myself:

Neighborhood News

Many people live in a neighborhood. A neighborhood is made up of people who live and work close to each other.

A neighborhood may include stores. It may have a park. There may be houses or apartment buildings—or some of both. Do you live in a neighborhood or have you visited one?

Make a chart like the one below. You can add headings or change them. Fill in the chart and put it in a safe place.

Take a neighborhood trip on the pages ahead. Meet your neighbors, look at the buildings, and see how you fit into this important place.

You can preview this section by reading the activity titles and looking at the pictures. Choose the activities that look like fun and get started!

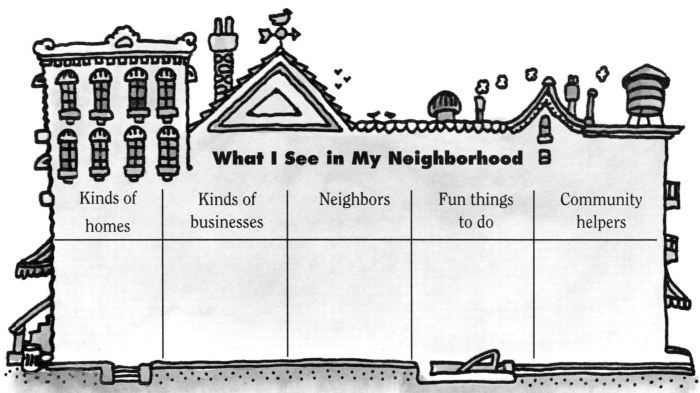

What I See in My Neighborhood

Kinds of homes	Kinds of businesses	Neighbors	Fun things to do	Community helpers

A Home in a Box

YOU NEED:
- ★ Shoeboxes, one for each floor of your home
- ★ Glue
- ★ Adhesive contact paper (optional)
- ★ Construction paper
- ★ Scissors
- ★ Paint

Every neighborhood is full of people. Almost everybody lives somewhere, in some kind of home.

There are many different kinds of homes. Some people live in houses. Others live in apartment buildings or trailer homes. Still others live on houseboats. What kind of home do you live in?

Here's a way to make your home out of boxes.

1. Take the lids off your shoeboxes. Stack them like this. Glue them in place.

2. Cover the outside with adhesive contact paper or construction paper. Or paint it to make it look like the outside of a home.

3. Think of each box as one floor of your home, or one apartment unit in your building. Cut shapes out of construction paper for windows, wallpaper, pictures, and anything else you can think of to decorate your walls.

4. Look around for small objects to decorate your home, such as:

★ Small boxes (for tables and beds)
★ Spools of thread (for chairs)
★ Scraps of cloth (for tablecloths, curtains, and bedspreads)
★ Artificial flowers
★ Small plastic toys
★ Pipe cleaners (for fuzzy furniture)
★ Cotton balls (for pillows)

Be creative! Your home can be as plain or as fancy as you want. Make each floor different to display all the floors of your house or apartment building.

Study Tip: Using What You Know

What's it like to do something for the first time? Does it make you a little nervous or excited? Sometimes you can use something you already know to understand something new. For example, you can use what you know about hitting a baseball to help you hit a tennis ball. The swing is different. The balls are different. But one thing is the same. You've got to keep your eye on the ball. When you're trying something for the first time, ask yourself:

★ Have I done something like this?
★ Have I read about this in books or heard about it on TV?
★ Have I seen anything like this?
★ What else do I know that might be useful?

Then think about the ways in which the new situation is like the one you already knew about. How are the two situations different? Use what you know to help you learn about what you don't know!

Map Your Neighborhood

YOU NEED:

★ A sketch pad
★ A pencil
★ Graph paper
★ A ruler
★ Colored markers

Suppose relatives from another town came to visit and didn't know their way around. You could make them a map. A map would show them where important places are—and how to get to them.

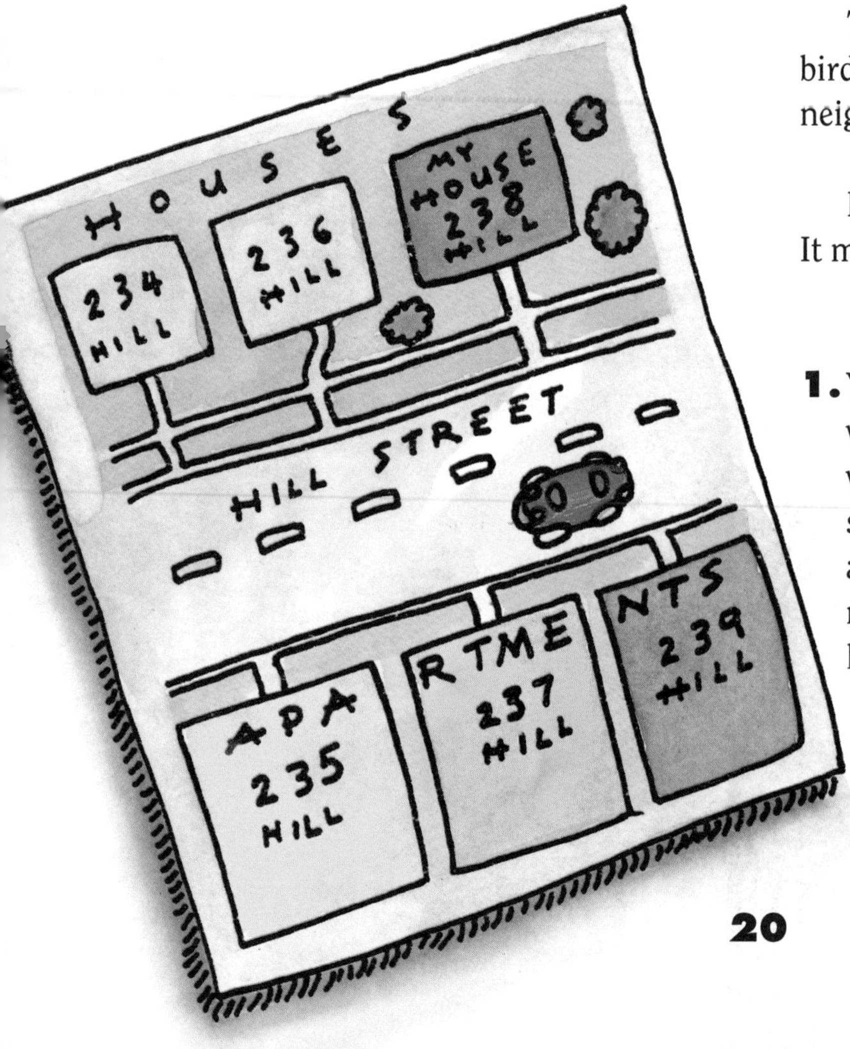

To learn how maps work, think like a bird! Imagine you're flying above your neighborhood. What do you see?

Look at this map of a neighborhood. It might give you some ideas.

1. You might want to start by taking a walk through your neighborhood with a parent. Bring your sketch pad so you can jot down what you see and where it is. As you look around, note where certain buildings or landmarks are located.

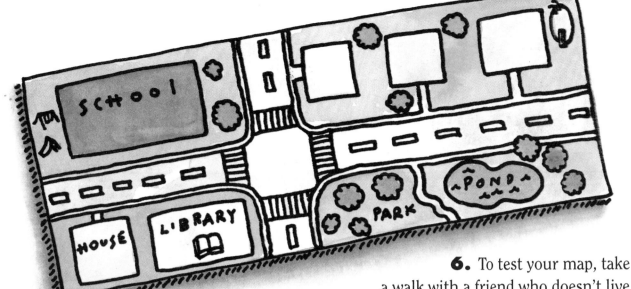

2. When you return, draw the outline of your home on graph paper. Use a pencil so you can erase things later if you need to.

3. Draw a line for your street. Then map the homes or buildings on either side of your home. You might want to label them.

4. Next, map whatever is across the street from you.

You can map as many of the buildings, parks, and streets in your neighborhood as you like. The more you include on your map, the easier it will be for people to find their way around.

If you want to map a lot of buildings, make everything small enough to fit.

5. When your map is finished, decorate it with colored markers.

6. To test your map, take a walk with a friend who doesn't live in your neighborhood. (Take a parent along too.) Ask your friend to find the way to a certain place by using your map.

Study Tip: Use Maps

People use maps to find their way around. Maps can show small areas, such as a neighborhood, or large areas, such as the world.

★ All maps have symbols. Some symbols are shaped like roads, mountains, campsites or other things shown on the map. They appear in a box called the *map key*.

★ Most maps show a bird's-eye view— a view of a place as it is seen from above.

Find several maps and compare them. How are they the same? How are they different?

Playground Play

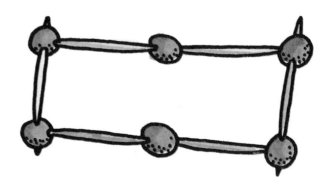

YOU NEED:
★ Modeling clay or soft wax
★ Toothpicks
★ Glue

Many neighborhoods have a playground. Did you see one on your walk? Is it in a park or a schoolyard? What equipment does your playground have? A slide? A seesaw? Swings? What else?

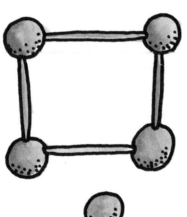

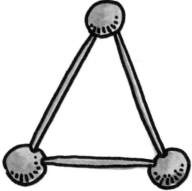

Visit your neighborhood playground. Try out the equipment. When you come home, make a miniature playground. Here's how.

1. Roll the clay or soft wax into pea-sized balls.

2. Stick a toothpick into a ball of clay. Then put another ball on the other end. Stick in another toothpick. Make some shapes like these:

22

3. Once you have the hang of it, try making some more complex shapes, like these:

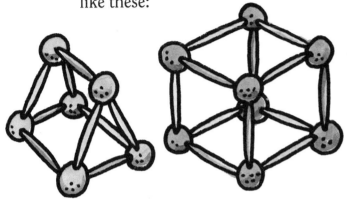

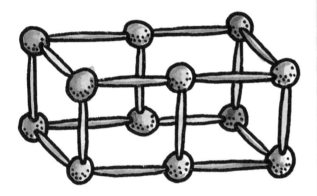

4. If you want to make a level surface, glue toothpicks side by side, like this:

5. Now you're ready to make some playground equipment. How many different structures can you make?

Study Tip: Figure Things Out

Was it hard for you to make the toothpick structures? What do you do when something seems too hard? Here are some things to think about.

★ Make sure you understand the directions. Read them over again and follow them in order.

★ If you still don't understand, ask for help. If you still can't do it, ask yourself, "Have I done my best?" If your answer is "yes," relax. Everybody finds some things easy and some things hard. Try again another day.

A Neighborhood Post Office

YOU NEED:
- ★ Scissors
- ★ Shoeboxes
- ★ Stickers, crayons, old mail with stamps
- ★ Paper
- ★ Old magazines
- ★ Junk mail
- ★ Envelopes
- ★ Play money
- ★ Tape

Visit your neighborhood post office. What goes on there?

Post offices are very important places. Post offices collect everyone's mail and sort it out. Mail carriers deliver the mail to the right addresses.

Make your own post office. Then *you* can be in charge of the mail.

1. Find a table, a chair, and a place where you can play for a while.

2. To make a mailbox, ask a grown-up to cut a slot in one of the shoeboxes.

3. Use the other shoeboxes for sorting the mail. For example, you can use one box for your mail, one for your mother's mail, and one for a friend's mail. Write name labels on the boxes so you know where each person's mail goes.

4. Make stamps. Use stickers, draw pictures on small squares of paper, or cut used stamps off old mail.

5. Now make some mail!

★ Write a flier about a garage sale.
★ Write a post card. Pretend you're on a trip and tell a friend about it.
★ Copy a bill. Send it to your parents.
★ Make a magazine! Write some stories. Draw pictures or cut out pictures from old magazines. (Get permission first.) Staple the pages together, and send the magazine to your parents or best friend.

6. Open up the post office for business! Sell your friends stamps and direct them to the mailbox to mail their letters. Sort out the mail and make deliveries.

Study Tip: Share Your Work

When you make something you want to share with others, it's important to do your best. For example, if you write a letter or a story, you need to write clearly. You want the person who reads it to understand every word.

★ Look at your words. Are any of them hard to read?
★ Are there spaces between all your words?
★ Did you start each sentence with a capital letter and end it with a period, question mark, or exclamation mark?

Use your eraser and make any changes you need to make.

Whatever you share, if it's a painting, a song, or a dance, make sure you feel ready to have others see it. If there are things that you want to change, make the changes before you share.

Neighborhood Patchwork

YOU NEED:

★ Plain paper
★ Colored markers or crayons
★ Clear tape

Look at your "What I See in My Neighborhood" chart. Do you want to add any new information? Do you need to change anything?

Many people work in your neighborhood. You've probably seen police officers, store owners, mail carriers, crossing guards, teachers, doctors, and dentists. Who else works in your neighborhood?

To help you think about who is who in your neighborhood, add the new information to your chart. Then use the chart to help you decide what kind of paper patchwork you want to make.

1. Choose one thing or person from each category—or all the things or people from all the categories. Decide how big you want your patchwork to be.

2. Draw a picture of each thing or person on separate pieces of paper. Write a label that tells what—or who—it is.

3. When you have drawn all your pictures, tape them together to make a wallhanging.

You may want to give your patchwork to the public library. They can display your neighborhood patchwork for the whole community to enjoy.

Study Tip: Getting More Information

Were all your questions about your neighborhood answered? If not, you might need to do some research! Here are some ways to get information:

★ Ask yourself what books might have the information you need. An encyclopedia? Another kind of book? Then go to a library.

★ Get information from the source. That is, if you're trying to find out who works in your neighborhood, take a walk and look around. What stores do you see? Who works in them? Keep a list.

★ Ask people what they know. A friend or a parent may know something you don't about your neighborhood.

How to Make a Book

YOU NEED:

★ 1 sheet of construction paper (9 inches by 12 inches)
★ 3 sheets of white paper (8-1/2 inches by 11 inches)
★ A stapler

Learn how to make a book about your neighbors, your family, or anything else you like!

1. First, fold the sheets of white paper neatly in half.

2. Then fold the sheet of construction paper in half.

3. Put the construction paper over the white papers to make a cover.

4. Staple close to the folds.

You can make a bigger book in almost the same way.

1. Use five or six sheets of white paper—or as many pages as you want. Don't fold them.

2. Place two pieces of construction paper over the white paper to make the cover. Staple at the left edges. Or, punch three holes through all the pages and tie them together with yarn.

Once you know how to make books, you can make them in any size and use any kind of paper. You can also make them in different shapes.

Here are some different kinds of books you can make.

Address Book

Do you have friends and neighbors you call on the phone or write letters to? An address book is a good place to keep their names, phone numbers, and addresses.

1. Make a list of the people you want to include in your address book.

2. Ask people to write down their addresses and phone numbers. Or, if you prefer, you can put the names in alphabetical order. Make sure your book has at least 13 pages. Write two letters at the top of each page in alphabetical order. For example, write AB on the first page and CD on the second page. Look at the first letter of each person's last name to decide which page to put their address on.

Counting Book

Do you have a younger brother or sister who is just learning to count? Make a counting book to help him or her learn numbers!

1. Make a book that has at least 10 pages.

2. Write the numbers in order, with one on each page. Also write the number words.

3. Draw objects on each page to show each number.

Photo Album

1. Find photographs you like—pictures of yourself, your family, a trip you took, or anything else.

2. With your parents' permission, tape one photograph to each page.

3. Write a sentence or two telling what each photo shows.

Picture Book

1. Make up a story. Write part of the story on each page. Then draw pictures to illustrate each scene.

2. Think of a good title and write it on the cover. Put your name on the cover too, so everyone will know you wrote the book.

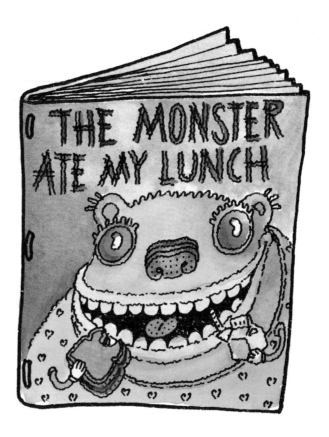

Journal

A journal is a special book just for your ideas and thoughts.

1. Make a very special book and find a special place to keep it.

2. Each day, write something in your journal. You might write about something that happened that day. You might write down an idea for a story. You might write lists of things you plan to do or things you'd like to learn.

What **D**o **Y**ou **T**hink?

Now that you've been around your neighborhood, write or draw
your answers to these questions.

Did you need help with any of the activities? Which ones?

Who helped you?

Which activity was easy for you?